GOLDINGS, NAPOLEONS AND ROMNEYS

Kent Black pigs in a cherry orchard c1911

The Story of Farming in Kent

Alan Major

Illustrati~~

C/S12855 77

By the same author
Cherries in the Rise. S B Publications
Hidden Kent. Countryside Books
A New Dictionary of Kent Dialect. Meresborough Books
Who's Buried Where in Kent. Meresborough Books

First published in 1999 by S. B. Publications,
c/o 19 Grove Road, Seaford, East Sussex BN25 1TP

ISBN 1 85770 150 X

Designed and typeset by CGB, Lewes
Printed by Adland Print Group
Unit 10-11, Bellingham Trading Estate, Franthorne Way, London SE6 3BX
Tel: 0181-695 6262 Fax: 0181-695 6300

CONTENTS

	Page
Acknowledgements	4
1 CROPS OF KENT	
Hops	5
2 CROPS OF KENT	
Cherries	13
3 CROPS OF KENT	
Apples	17
4 CROPS OF KENT	
Fruit	21
Cobnuts and filberts	23
5 EXOTIC CROPS	
Lavender	27
Peppermint	30
Mangolds, white mustard and woad	32
6 LIVESTOCK	
Kentish Red cattle	35
7 LIVESTOCK	
Kentish pigs	37
8 LIVESTOCK	
Orpington poultry	41
9 LIVESTOCK	
Kent sheep	45
10 IMPLEMENTS	
Ploughs	51
Hoes	56
Hop garden implements	57
Cutting tools	62
Bibliography	64

ACKNOWLEDGEMENTS

THE author tenders his grateful thanks to the following for their generous assistance to him in the preparation and illustrat ion of this book:

Dr Joan Morgan, Brogdale Horticultural Trust, Faversham, for reading and advising on the apple chapter and for permission to quote from *Book of Apples* by Dr Morgan and Alison Richards and its directory of apple varieties section.

Eddie Barton, Herne, for advice and the loan of material; Leslie Barton, Maidstone, for information regarding the Kent plough;Brian Self, Brogdale Horticultural Trust, Faversham, for information on plums.

Meg Game, Oldbury Farmhouse, Ightham, and the secretary of the Kentish Cobnuts Association, Clakkers House, Crouch, Sevenoaks for information on cobnuts and filberts; C F Hickman, Stelling Minnis, for information on Kent Pigs; E S Adams, Halstead,

PICTURE CREDITS

THE author is most grateful to Richard Filmer, Kennington, Ashford, for the loan of numerous photographs, also to Jo English, Waterlooville; Meg Game, Oldbury Farmhouse, Ightham and A G Turner, Petts Wood.

Pictures that do not bear an individual credit are from the author's own collection.

Front cover: (top) Oxon team, Tenterden, c.1905.
(bottom left) Tallyman and binmen in hop gardens.
(bottom right) Interior of an Oast house, showing dried hops.
Back cover: (top) Buff Orpingtons.
(bottom) A Kent plough.

1

THE CROPS OF KENT

Hops

*Kent, sir, everybody knows Kent – apples, cherries,
hops and women. Charles Dickens*

SO said Mr Jingle in *The Pickwick Papers.* He could have added sheep for the Romney breed is equally famous throughout the world. However, there have been other crops and livestock, tools and implements that are less well known but equally important to the farming history of Kent. But let us start with hops.

In early hop cultivation the bines or climbing shoots were trained up straight ash or chestnut poles from 12ft to l6ft high. The poles were usually obtained from the periodic coppicing of the sweet chestnut and mixed species plantations in Kent, a source still in use today. There were two, three or four poles per 'hill' each with a bine growing from the hop plant. The term 'hill' arose because at this time the poles and hop plants were established in low, hill-like mounds of earth. This method continued for several centuries and as recently as 1911 Hall and Russell recorded that the system survived 'in backward parts of the Weald . . . where farmers have five to ten acres of hops.'

About 1874 Thomas Coley devised his patent 'vinery system' of hop cultivation. In this either side of each 'hill' two poles about eight feet high, each topped with a fork made of metal wire lashed to the pole, were planted firmly in the earth. About a third of their height from the ground the two poles were joined by a crosspiece from which two shorter poles were positioned diagonally with their upper ends resting in the forks of the poles opposite. Around each one of these diagonal poles a hop bine was trained.

The advantages claimed for Coley's system was that the poles were more secure and as the hops hung down from the diagonal crosspieces into an open area they were not battered against the poles. However, it cost more than £70 an acre to set up the system and so its use was not universal in Kent.

It was superseded by the 'wirework' system which used taller chestnut poles. They were four inches in diameter at the base and tapered to about three inches in diameter at summit and strong galvanised wire was attached to them in a grid pattern, started horizontally near ground level, with a second wire at chest height and a third near the top of the poles, some 13ft from the ground. This is probably the system anyone hop picking between the wars will remember.

A group of five binmen, c 1907, each holding a hop hook. Binmen acted as assistants to the measurer when picked hops measured from each picker's bin or basket..

Several different systems of stringing the hops were developed. One in Kent was the Butcher system which required three or four strings of coir, one per shoot, to be tied from the bottom wire to the chest high wire and then, at an angle across the alley space between the hop plants and wirework rows, to the wire near the top of the neighbouring row of poles and wires. The top stringing was done by men on stilts and the lower layers by others standing on the ground. Up each coir string women workers trained a hop bine to spiral upwards.

A load of freshly picked hops about to be hauled by a team of oxen to an oast house for drying. *Photo: Richard Filmer.*

A description of the Butcher system of stringing is given by Hall and Russell:

'From this top wire every year coir yarn is strung down to the ground, two, three or four strings being led to each hill; different patterns of lacing are adopted but they all have this in common that the strings run at a slope of between fifty and sixty degrees with the horizontal, but never vertically.'

No one man can be said to have introduced the 'wirework' system, but as Henry Butcher of Selling (some sources say 'of Sheldwich'), near Faversham, in 1875 did much to introduce it and the method of stringing used with it, and to publicise it in Kent, his name has remained associated with it.

The 'wirework' system of hop growing, which required far fewer poles, cost about £50 an acre in 1884 and was down to £30 an acre in 1911. Even with the extra annual expense of coir stringing at £2 10s or more an acre, it resulted in higher quality hops and it rapidly became popular in all Kent's hop growing districts, especially east Kent. It is still in use today but has mainly been replaced by the 'umbrella' system in which three or four strings from the hill are tied together at chest height and then spread out at an angle to give an umbrella shape.

7

A stilt walker in a hop garden near Faversham tying the strings of the Butcher system. *Photo: Richard Filmer*

The different varieties of hops grown from the original wild hop, *Humulus lupulus,* were the result of selective development and trial cultivation. The object of the trials was to produce healthy plants that would give either heavy early, main or late crop; suit the different soils of the area; and fulfill brewers' requirements as to flavour. Some varieties had a short career until replaced by improved varieties, while others remained in cultivation for many years.

Hops with Kent origins

Amos's Early Bird
A variety resembling the Bramling, bred by Alfred Amos of Wye.

Apple Puddings
An old variety formerly grown in the Weald. Its origin is unknown.

Bates' Brewers
Main crop, discovered by John Bates of Brenchley in a hop garden in Sevenoaks in 1879 or 1880. Although a good quality hop with plenty of lupulin and a good flavour it was a light cropper.

Bennett's Early Seedling
This early variety had medium sized cones,a good lupulin content and flavour and it preferred stiff soils. Raised from seed by a Mr Bennett of Wrotham.

Bramling
An early variety discovered by a farm bailiff named Smith on the farm of Musgrave Hilton at Bramling, near Canterbury. From 1865 it was widely cultivated in the best hop growing areas of Mid Kent and into the Weald and in Sussex. It was a red-bined hop, the compact cone having petals and flavour similar to Golding, but it was hardier and earlier than that variety.

Buss's Golding
Late. Found about 1869 in the Lyminge area by a Mr Buss of Elphicks, Horsmonden, and successfully cultivated by him. It was a red-bined, hardy hop with small cones with thin, pale petals shaped like those of Golding,

Canterbury Grape
Main crop, an improved Grape Hop.

Canterbury Jacks
A late variety, known as Buss's Golding when grown in other areas.

Canterbury Whitebine
A variety of Old Golding, (see Whitebine).
Cobb's Hop.
Main crop, introduced about 1881 by John Cobb, Sheldwich and grown extensively in east Kent, mid Kent, the Weald and in Sussex. It had a good flavour and was like Golding in form but a coarser, stronger hop.
Colegate or Colegate's Hop
A late variety introduced about 1805 by David Colgate or Colegate of Chevening. It had coarse flavoured hop cones which were long and narrow and it was said to have come from a wild hop plant found in a farm hedge at Chevening. It did well on the clay soils in Kent and Sussex.
Flemish Red Bine
An early variety with large cones, but it was deficient in lupulin.
Fuggle's Hop
Main crop. The original hop bine is reputed to have been found in a garden at Horsmonden and was introduced about 1875 by Richard Fuggle of Brenchley. It is also said to have originated from a hop seed found in the dinner basket of a hop picker and thrown down with crumbs on George Stace's farm at Horsmonden in 1861 and was then raised and introduced commercially by Fuggle. It is grown particularly on stiff soils in mid Kent, the Kent Weald and in Sussex and is a vigorous, hardy variety. Its large hop cones with pointed petals are strongly flavoured.
Golden Tips
A very old variety, origin unknown.
Golding, Old Golding
Main crop. Raised about 1790 by a Mr Golding of Malling to become commonly cultivated in the best hop soil districts, in particularly east Kent, less so in mid Kent. This superior variety had large hop cones with rounded, much-veined petals and a delicate flavour.
Grape Hop
A main crop hop with cones squarish in cross-section growing on very short branches so they crowd together and look like bunches of grapes.
Henham's Jones's Hop
An early raised by Mr Iden Henham of East Peckham. It was rather a curiosity with a thin, pale bine and hop cones that were golden when ripe.
Hobbs's Early
Origin unknown.

Late Red Bine
Similar to Buss's Golding/Canterbury Jacks.
Meopham
Early hop with a red bine bearing large, coarse, medium-flavoured hops low in lupulin content. It was possibly developed from the Flemish Red bine.
Mercer's Hop
Main crop. Obtained from a hop garden at Malling about 1880and developed by R M Mercer, Rodmersham House, Sittingbourne. Its heavy-bearing bines had hops with a high content of lupulin.
Old Jones's Hop
Main crop. A medium sized, good shaped and flavoured hop on short green bines but with a low yield in cones. It was being grown in Kent in 1798 when it bore the name, Jones's Hop, but who Jones was has not yet been discovered.
Petham Golding
Another name for Canterbury Whitebine, (which see).
Pretty Wills
Late. Grown in Kent but origin unknown.
Prolific
An early. The original hop bine is reputed to have been found by Thomas Guest of Chill Mill Farm, Brenchley in a hop garden planted with Old Jones's Hop. It was raised by him in 1852. The hop cones are large, have an orange tint when mature and contain numerous purple coloured seed, but are deficient in flavour. The bine is red.
Rodmersham
Another name for Mercer's Hop (which see).
Ruflers
Late. Grown in Kent but origin unknown.
Seale's Early Golding
Raised by a Mr Seale of Horsmonden.
Tolhurst Hop
An early prolific, heavy yielding, good flavoured variety for clay soil, raised in the early 1880s by James Tolhurst of Horsmonden.
Tutsham Hop
Main crop. Raised by a Gerald Warde of Tutsham Hall and cultivated in the hop gardens of Tutsham Farm, West Farleigh. It had the character, flavour and shape of Golding.

11

Waring's Imperial
A very old variety, formerly grown in the Weald. Origin unknown.
Whitebine
Main crop to late. A variety of Golding with a delicate flavour grown mainly in the Canterbury area as it suited the dry soils and climate of the district.
White's Early
Introduced in 1852 by George White of Hunton, Maidstone and then considered to be the best early hop variety. The cones were pale golden with a good flavour, but yield tended to fluctuate.
Williams' Hop
A very old, late variety, possibly introduced into Kent from Farnham, Surrey.

Hop (*Humulus lupulus*).

Women cherry pickers with their kibsy baskets, *c* 1910

2
THE CROPS OF KENT
Cherries

If they blow in April
You'll have your fill
But if in May,
They'll all go away.

THE two wild cherries growing in Kent – the Gean and Dwarf or Wild Cherry – would have been noted by the Romans during their occupation of the county for they cultivated cherries in Italy and in other parts of Europe. It is therefore likely that they introduced varieties to cultivate around their settlements and possibly cross-bred them with better examples of the wild cherries to improve the latter – a policy that may have also been practised by early Kent growers. After the Roman withdrawal in 406 AD it is likely cherry cultivation was neglected and little is known of it until the fourteenth century when cherries are recorded as being grown on the estate by the monks of Teynham manor, an archiepiscopal palace owned by the Archbishop and Christ Church, Canterbury, to which some of the produce was dispatched. A proportion may have also been sold as income for the manor, but commercial cultivation in Kent is not firmly recorded, although there can be little doubt that it was taking place.

In 1680 Thomas Fuller, in his *Worthies of Kent,* credits Flemish refugees with introducing cherries to Kent in the mid-sixteenth century. John Aubrey in his *Brief Lives* says:

'Cherries were first brought in to Kent in the reign of Henry VIII, the king being in Flanders and liking the cherries, ordered his gardener, Richard Harrys, to bring them hence and propagate in England. This Harrys did, on land granted by the king, at Teynham, from 1533.'

Soon cherry cultivation was to spread to thirty other parishes, from Rainham to Blean Wood and by the end of the eighteenth century had

Osier Farm, Teynham was the site of the first commercial cherry orchard in Kent. It was still producing cherries when this photograph was taken in the 1980s.

expanded from Canterbury to the Cherry Garden Lane area of Folkestone; around Maidstone; into the Weald;from the Gravesend area to Swanscombe; to Dartford and Crayford to east London.

Expansion continued into the nineteenth century to meet the demand from London and northern England markets. Early in the twentieth century many of the older orchards were grubbed out and replanted with newer varieties and these young trees were maturing in the Second World War and late 1940s. After that cherry cultivation gradually declined f or various reasons – diseased trees, shortage of pickers, loss of markets, high costs of production, or superseded by apple and other crops

In the past cherry cultivation was labour intensive. Men and women pickers were required at the critical time in the fruit's maturing. Some varieties had trees as high or higher than houses and ladders with sixty or sixty-five rungs were needed to reach the crop. The cherries were hand picked into kibsy baskets worn on the picker's back and they were transferred to half-sieve baskets (later chip baskets) to be taken to market by rail or lorry. However, in the 1970s the development of new dwarfing rootstocks began and they have made it possible for the pickers to reach the fruit from short ladders, trestles and from the ground. The new shrub type trees will be easier to maintain as they are low enough to be covered by nets to protect the fruit from the bird predators. The re-emergence of cherry cultivation as an economic crop in Kent is again a possibility.

More than a thousand varieties of cherries have been named worldwide, but only a fraction of these were cultivated in Britain. The Brogdale Horticultural Trust's National Cherry Collection at Faversham has some 220 varieties in its care so they do not become extinct. Examples are:

Amber
White, early, cultivated in Kent from the mid-eighteenth century.
Black Tartarian
Introduced from Russia in 1796.
Bradbourne Black
Bred at the East Malling Research Station's headquarters at Bradbourne House.
Early Rivers
Raised from a seed of Early Purple Guigne by Thomas Rivers as a very early black and introduced in 1872.

Flemish Red
Possibly one of the varieties imported by Richard Harrys from Flanders in 1533, and termed 'a Flemish cherry'.

Florence
Usually the last cherry variety picked in a normal season, early August.

Frogmore Early
Raised by Thomas Ingram, Queen Victoria's head gardener at Frogmore,and introduced about 1864.

Governor Wood
An American variety, raised in 1842 by a Professor Kirtland in Cleveland, Ohio. It was named after Reuben Wood, Governor of Ohio and was grown in Kent to rival Frogmore as a second early white variety.

Kentish Red
Similar to Flemish Red and was being grown in Kent at least by the eighteenth century, possibly earlier,

May Duke or The Duke
A hybrid of sweet cherry, *Prunus avium,* and acid culinary *Prunus cerasus.* One of the first cherry varieties bred in Kent and not imported, although there is a belief it arrived from France about 150 years ago, the name being a corruption of Medoc, the region where it supposedly originated.

Merton Biggareau
Raised by John Innes Horticultural Institute, 1924.

Morello
Known to Gerard, author of a famous *Herball* of 1597. It became more popular in eighteenth century, sometimes also being known as Morella or Milan cherry. Used by Thomas Grant in the 1840s to make his famous Morella Cherry Brandy, firstly at Dover then by the company at Maidstone until 1960.

Napoleon Bigarreau
First recorded as Lauermann Bigarreau in Germany and introduced into England in 1832.

Ohio Beauty
Raised by Professor Kirtland in Cleveland and brought to England in 1847.

Waterloo
Raised by Thomas Andrew Knight, at Elton Hall, Ludlow. Bore fruit for the first time just before the battle, hence its name. Introduced into Kent, 1815.

3

THE CROPS OF KENT

Apples

Christmas and a little before,
The apple goes and not the core;
Christmas and a little later,
The apple goes and the core comes after.

THIS Kentish saying is a reminder of the days when apples were so plentiful before Christmas that only the flesh was consumed, but after Christmas there were not so many available and so every bit was eaten – including the core.

A Faversham doctor, Edward Jacob, was the first to record the wild or crab apple, *Malus sylvestris/Malus pumila,* growing in Kent. In his *Plantae Favershamienses, a catalogue of the plants growing spontaneously about Faversham* in 1777, he refers to it as: '*Malus sylvestris.* In Hedges. Not uncommon.'

It was certainly growing long before that as 'a native county tree, in woods, hedges, though less common now than in the past,' according to Hanbury and Marshall in their *Flora of Kent* of 1899. On or near Roman sites in Kent seeds of *Malus sylvestris* have been found. They probably came from local trees, but the Romans, who had been growing and cross-breeding apple varieties since the fourth century AD, were supposedly not too keen on eating the wild apple. It is likely, therefore, that they brought some of their cultivated varieties to this country to supply them with the type of apples they preferred.

One variety believed to have been grown by the Romans is Court Pendu Plat which is suitable for planting in frost pockets as it is a late flowering dessert variety. It produces medium-sized, short-stalked greenish-yellow to bright yellow red striped apples which are picked in October for ripening in December/January. The Court Pendu Plat had been introduced to Kent from France by the eighteenth century and is still occasionally cultivated.

Apple picking at Pluckley. *Photo: Richard Filmer*

Another variety cultivated in Kent as far back as the thirteenth century was the large, ribbed, greenish-yellow, culinary Costard. From the fourteenth century to the sixteenth century, however, little is recorded about apple cultivation in the county although the dialect used by 'Mayster Jon Gardener in his poem *The Feate of Gardeninge* indicates this fifteenth century writer was from the county or the southeast and that Kent orchards in that time were supplying apples and other fruit to markets in London.

The Kent fruit orchards were considerably extended in the eighteenth century to meet the increasing demand of London's markets. There was a further rapid expansion from 1820 when a tariff was placed on the import of foreign apples which encouraged growers to plant new orchards. At the beginning of the twentieth century demand for Kent culinary apples rose and many new orchards were established mainly with

Bramley's Seedling. The expansion of apple cultivation has continued in Kent since the Second World War – at the expense of reduction of cherry tree acreage.

In the past, at times when apple growers in Kent could not find a sale for a crop, they resourcefully made cider from it, which, in some cases, was given to their labourers instead of the daily beer allowance. It was also sold in markets and in towns nearest to the orchards. Unlike counties that used cider apples for making cider in Kent it was made from sundry varieties, in particular culinary apples.

The areas most favoured for apples and other fruit are detailed by Hall and Russell in their *Report on the Agriculture and Soils of Kent*, 1911

'The fruit area forms a band starting out from south-east of London and following the belt of free-working loams on the Thanet sands and chalk as far as the Medway valley. The Medway Valley forms the nucleus of another area, a large proportion of the land on the Lower Greensand (ragstone) on either side of the Valley west of Maidstone is in fruit. When the Medway valley opens out in the Weald Clay plain, fruit still follows its course on the alluvial soil and even on to the sands and clays of the High Weald. East of the Medway Valley one of the richest areas of fruit land is formed by the deep loams of the Thanet Sand, chalk and brick-earth, which stretches from Rochester through Sittingbourne to Canterbury, while beyond Canterbury fruit continues to follow the outcrop of the Thanet Sands through Wingham and Wickham round to Ash and Sandwich.'

That Kent was indeed suitable is indicated by the considerable number of apples with Kent origins or association. The National Apple Collection at Brogdale Farm, Faversham, has more than 2,000 varieties. Among them are:

Allington Pippin
Late dessert culinary apple raised by Thomas Laxton in Lincolnshire before 1884 and named South Lincoln Pippin. It was introduced into Kent in 1896 by George Bunyard of Maidstone, who renamed it in 1894 after his fruit tree nursery at Allington.

Beauty of Kent
Late culinary, but if stored can be an eating apple in November/December. Existed in a London nursery in the 1820s and one of the common culinary apples grown in country house gardens in Kent in the Victorian period.

Bramley's Seedling
Late culinary. F Smith of Loddington near Maidstone planted the first commercially grown examples in Kent in 1890.

Diamond Jubilee
Late dessert culinary. May have been raised by a Mr Thomas of Rainham in 1889. Gained the Royal Horticultural Society Award of Merit in 1901.

Faversham Creek
Mid-season culinary. Discovered growing near Faversham Creek by H Ermen in the 1970s.

Gascoyne's Scarlet
Mid-season dessert. Raised by Mr Gascoyne, of a family involved with fruit farming in Kent for several generations at Bapchild Court, Sittingbourne, and introduced in 1871 by George Bunyard of Maidstone.

George Neal
Early dessert culinary raised by a Mrs Reeves of Otford in 1904 but named after the nurseryman who introduced it – George Neal of Wandsworth.

Isaac Newton's Tree (Flower of Kent)
Mid-season culinary. The tree was growing in the garden at Woolsthorpe Manor, near Grantham in 1665and Isaac Newton saw an apple fall from it and this gave him the 'notion' of the law of gravity. The original tree died in 1814 but had been propagated and so it survives in several places. It produces a large, ribbed apple apparently identical to that of the Flower of Kent growing in Kent in the seventeenth century, which is available from specialist fruit tree nurseries. The Isaac Newton is obtainable from the Brogdale Plant Centre.

Kentish Codlin
A codlin-type apple assumed to have originated in Kent, hence its name. Illustrated in John Parkinson's *Paradisus Terrestris* of 1629.

Maid of Kent
Late culinary. The original sixty year old tree was growing on Sheephurst Farm, Marden, where scion wood was obtained from the owner, D G Jenner, in 1979 for the National Apple Collection, Brogdale.

Maidstone Favourite
Early dessert. Raised by George Bunyard, Maidstone.

Tydeman's Late Orange
Late dessert. Raised at East Malling Research Station by H M Tydeman in 1930 and introduced 1949. A keeping apple, up to March, the flesh becoming a strong yellow, hence its name.

Others developed and grown, or just grown, in Kent include: Cobham, Kentish Fillbasket, Colonel Vaughan (Kentish Pippin), Folkestone, Hunt's Early, Great Expectations, Kentish Quarrenden, Loddington and South Park.

4
THE CROPS OF KENT

Fruit and nuts

AS well as the 'sweet cherry, temperate pippin and golden renate' Henry VIII's gardener, Richard Harris, planted varieties of pears imported from France at Teynham in 1533 and their cultivation spread to the other fruit growing areas of Kent. A variety cultivated in the seventeenth century was Uvedale's St Germain, a cooking pear which was still being grown in the 1940s and even recommended by Raymond Bush, a fruit authority of that time, as one of the six best cooking pears. Dr Uvedale was a schoolmaster at Eltham, which was then in Kent, and he raised the pear in 1690. It is pale yellow with russetting around the eye, and usually very large and heavy.

Conference, still a popular pear, was first commercially grown in Kent although it was raised by Francis Rivers of Rivers fruit tree specialists of Sawbridgeworth. In 1895 Rivers sent the first twenty-five Conference pear trees as a gift to Edmonds of Allington, near Maidstone. They tried them in their orchards where they were very successful and in a short time Edmonds was the first commercial grower of the variety.

The Diamond or Black Diamond Plum is a cooking variety, blue-black with a bloom, that was formerly much cultivated in Kent but less so now. It originated in the county – from a chance seedling found in a hedge at Brenchley by a farm worker named Diamond.

Picking Kentish Blue plums.
Photo: Richard Filmer

It was developed by a Brenchley nurseryman named Hooker who introduced it in 1830. Another plum that originated in Kent is the Kentish Bush which in some districts is called Waterloo or Kentish Blue. It was reputedly found in ahedge near Sittingbourne in 1836. The tree is tall and upright and the dark purple fruit has yellow or russet dots. At one time it was popular and grown in many orchards in the county but there are now few young trees under cultivation perhaps because the golden yellow flesh is rather dry and has little flavour.

The Farleigh Damson, known also as the Cluster Damson, was found as a wild seedling by James Crittenden of Farleigh who introduced it about 1820. It is a small, black, damson with a good flavour; a heavy cropper; and is still cultivated today.

One of the most popular gooseberries in commercial cultivation in the nineteenth century was Berry's Early Kent, which, with another called Keepsake, was first recorded in 1841. It was picked green and hard to get early market sales. Another was Careless, known to have been cultivated in the county before 1860.

Superlative, a dessert variety of raspberry, was raised by a Mr Merryfield at Waldershare Gardens near Dover around 1877. Eminent fruit breeder and nurseryman George Bunyard, of Maidstone, claimed Superlative produced three times the crop of any other raspberry variety and added it to his list in 1888. From the 1920s to 1950s several new raspberry varieties were raised by Norman Grubb at East Malling Research Station including Malling Promise and Malling Jewel.

A new variety of blackcurrant, Wellington, a cross between Boskoop Giant and Baldwin, a nineteenth century variety, was raised by Mr R Wellington, the first director of the research station, in 1913 and introduced for commercial cultivation in 1927.

Strawberries were cultivated wherever there were expanses of Thanet Sand beds – in North Kent and in East Kent around Ash and Sandwich but increasing demand from jam makers brought about the rapid expansion of strawberry growing closer to London, around Swanley and St Mary Cray. One grower in the 1880s had 2,000 acres of strawberries. His pickers started work at 3am so the strawberries would arrive at Covent Garden and other markets fresh for the early morning's soft fruit sales.

Kentish cobnut trees at primrose time at the Silverhill Plantation, Dunks Green, Plaxtol. *Photo: Meg Game.*

Kentish cobnuts and filberts

THE ancestors of Kent's cobnut and filberts were examples of wild hazel *Corylus avellana,* the common cobnut, found in copses, hedgerows and woodland edges, and gathered as a free harvest when ripe. Sometime in the late sixteenth or early seventeenth century, cuttings were taken from the trees bearing good quality nuts and planted and cultivated as a farmed crop.

Thomas Tusser in his *Five Hundred Pointes of Good Husbandrie* of 1573, listed red and white 'filbeardes' among the 'fruits' to be cultivated in a garden. Leonard Mascall of Plumpton, Sussex, in *The Booke of Arte and Maner, Howe to Plant and Graffe all Sortes of Trees* published in 1575, advised taking suckers from the roots of the 'hasel' nut to propagate. This was certainly an established practice by the mid-seventeenth century when John Evelyn observed in *Sylva* that in Kent the nut bushes were grown 12ft apart and limited by pruning to 5ft high, and trained with an 'open centre' a method continued into modern times.

John Boys in his *General View of the Agriculture of Kent* of 1794 said that in some areas it was customary to plant nut bushes, cherry and apple trees, also hops, close together. The nut bushes were cultivated in this way for about thirty years before the larger fruit trees overwhelmed them and they were grubbed out. Later it became the practice to plant nut trees in rows in separate plantations.

These plantations, called nut plats or platts, were in the main on the Lower Greensand ridge, east, west and south of Maidstone, and localised in the Ashford area usually on stony ground where other crops were less successful. In the eighteenth century there were extensive plantings of such varieties as the White or White-skinned filbert; Kentish filbert; the Red or Red-skinned filbert; Purple filbert; Aveline Blanche Longue; and Aveline Rouge. In 1816 the thin-shelled Cosford was introduced. It was a good pollinator of other varieties and still survives in some of the old Kent plats.

About 1830 a Mr Lambert, probably of Goudhurst, introduced a fine variety – the Lambert's Filbert. Filbert was the name given to nuts which were enclosed by long husks or 'full beards' which clearly projected beyond their outward ends. Lambert's Filbert, which is a true filbert, *Corylus maxima,* is sometimes incorrectly called the Kent or Kentish cobnut .

However, the Kentish cobnut was extensively grown well in to the twentieth century, replacing the White-skinned filbert and Kentish filbert. At one time there were about 7,000 acres of them in and around Maidstone from which peak their cultivation gradually declined to 732 acres in 1951, the last year the Ministry of Agriculture recorded nut acreage in its returns. By the 1920s farmers whose family had grown nuts for generations sentimentally retained up to fifty acres, some of the bushes being up to a 100 years old and continuing to give a good crop. However, when they declined they were not replaced.

The rising costs of managing and harvesting the bushes, mostly by hand, made nut cultivation uneconomic, and many of the plats were replaced with other crops. However, nuts are still cultivated in Kent today.

Some of the 1,500 cobnut trees planted nearly 100 years ago on a plat covering 6.5 acres at Belks, Otham. *Photo: Meg Game*

An estimated 150 acres of mainly Kentish cobnuts – with Cosford as a supplementary pollinator – are maintained by a number of specialist growers. The Brogdale Horticultural Trust, Faversham, has forty varieties in its filbert and cobnut collection.

When establishing a new plat, rooted cuttings from the parent bush or saplings propagated by layering in a small stoolbed are planted in the autumn at spaced intervals. When they are 6ft to 8ft tall the bushes are pruned and trained to allow in plenty of air and light to circulate through the branches. After five to seven years they begin to bear a nut crop of 3lbs to 4lbs per bush. From the tenth to fifteenth year a substantial crop is produced and the bushes will carry on fruiting for more than 100 years.

In the past, in early winter, the nut plats would be roughly dug by gangs of men using plat forks to turn over large clods for the frost to work on. Later Canterbury hoes were used to break down clods not reduced by frost

25

and the plats were worked over with plate hoes to keep the weeds down as much as possible. Today these jobs are done by mechanical means.

Every autumn the long, new growths or 'nut wands' were removed from the base of the filbert and cobnut bushes. This job was done with a wanding iron which was like a wood chisel on a long handle. A downward thrust with this tool would sever the wands which would not be wasted. Their thickest ends would be sharpened to a point and then they would be dried and tied in bundles to be used as plant stakes. Light pruning was usually done twice a year. In summer unwanted growth was removed by gloved fingers; in winter some of the oldest wood was pruned off with a knife to keep the tree 'open',

Traditionally the nuts were picked in three stages – known as firsting, seconding, and thirding. The first picking was when the husks were green and the kernels especially juicy and sweet. They would be plucked by hand in bunches of two, three or four nuts for the 'green nut trade' in late August. This was followed by seconding in late September when the husks were going or had gone brown. The brown nuts were ripe and could be shaken from the husks and picked up from the ground around the bush. There was also sometimes a thirding, when the bushes were shaken so that any remaining nuts would fall to the ground. Buckets or kibsy baskets of the nuts were tipped into hessian sacks or Dutch trays, and taken to the packhouse where they were riddled, the empty nuts sorted out, and then tipped into 10lb wooden trays to be weighed and lidded.

Today there are usually two pickings – firsting and seconding – although it is not unknown for there to be a thirding in a season of a bountiful crop. Sometimes the nuts from the seconding are not all sold on but kept back to be stored to sell at Christmas.

Cutting the lavender flowers at Grove Ferry in the 1920s.

Photo: Jo English

5
SOME EXOTIC CROPS
Lavender

Here's flowers for you. Hot lavender, mints, savory, marjoram. . .
Shakespeare. A Winter's Tale

THE Mitcham area of Surrey is traditionally known for the cultivation and use of lavender. It may therefore come as a surprise that lavender was grown in Kent for local use and to supply the demand from the Mitcham lavender trade. It was cultivated for its volatile oil at Grove Ferry near Canterbury from the mid-nineteenth century until the 1930s; between Swanley and Crockenhill in large quantities up to the 1930s; and at Ebbsfleet near Minster-in-Thanet until the late 1970s.

Lavender is so familiar as to not require description. The densely packed mauve to violet-tinted spikes of flowers are the source of the oil, which is harvested in August. The variety grown for oil was usually *Lavendula intermedia,* a cross between *Lavendula officinalis* and the broad-leaved lavender, *Lavendula latifolia.*

Soil and situation were important to its successful cultivation. Lavender grows best on thin, chalky, stony, well-drained soil, especially light loam upon chalk, although it can be grown on sandy loam dressed with lime or chalk, The soil should not be too fertile or the bushes will produce fewer flowers and more foliage. Dry, sunny exposed positions, preferably sloping southwards are ideal, especially if the plants are protected from summer winds by high hedges or rows of trees.

The method of cultivation was simple. Six to nine inch long shoots were obtained as cuttings from mature bushes in early spring and planted in a sheltered area. When rooted they were transplanted either in October or the following early spring. This process involved taking out every other plant from every row, and removing all the plants from every other row and transplanting them to form another growing area.

It was important to plant the lavender deep down and special 14inch long dibbers were used. The young plants were inserted in the earth to within two inches of the top shoot, then firmed in. In their first year in their permanent position they were not allowed to bloom but were kept trimmed with sheep-shears to encourage them to become bushy and produce more flowering shoots. Commercially cultivated bushes were seldom kept after their fifth year as their productivity declined. Cuttings were usually planted every year to ensure that there would be a continuous number of bushes supplying flowers.

When all the flowers on each spike were fully open they were ready for distilling. Women did the cutting with sharp, sometimes-toothed sickles. The sickle was held in the right hand, while the left hand firmly held a number of lavender spikes. The women wore gloves or had their knuckles bandaged and also wore long-sleeved blouses or cardigans to protect their arms from the rough foliage. Although it might seem to be a pleasant task the women had mixed feelings about it.. As with hop-picking, where the yellow lupuline from the hops cones stains hands and clothing, so with lavender. The scent of the lavender clung to the clothes, hands and hair of the cutters and wherever they went it gave away the fact they were employed in the lavender fields.

Cutting only took place in the sunshine. The cut heads and stems were laid on mats beside the rows of bushes and were covered to avoid scorching if it was too hot. The mats were rolled up in the cool late afternoon or early evening, before the dew fell, and carted to the still if the plants were being processed locally. If the grower had a contract with a commercial distillery some distance away the arrangement was that the cut crop would be collected or delivered as soon as possible as freshness was essential.

The harvested lavender in the Crockenhill-Swanley area was taken to various distillers in the Mitcham district, one being W J Bush who also imported peppermint from Kent. Potter and Moore produced the world famous Mitcham Lavender Water and also supplied lavender oil to other users, including Yardleys.

At Grove Ferry the lavender was for local use. In the nineteenth century a Mr Bing acquired the Grove Ferry Inn on the south bank of the Stour, plus its ferry rights and adjoining land, on seventeen acres of which he planted lavender. He built a small distillery and from his home grown crop produced lavender water which he sold at the inn. His two daughters, Marion and Annie Bing, took over the inn and the, by-then twenty-one acres of lavender, on the death their father. They continued to distil lavender water and oil which was sold in Canterbury and elsewhere in the area

When the lavender was in bloom it was an attractive sight and afternoon charabanc excursions brought trippers from Cliftonville, Margate and other resorts to see the the Grove Ferry lavender fields. In 1928 the plants were killed when the Stour overflowed its banks and the fields had to be replanted when the waters subsided.

In the 1930s partly due to the Depression, the number of visitors declined and with them demand for the lavender products. In 1934 the sisters became bankrupt and the inn, distillery and lavender fields were sold. All that remains of Grove Ferry's lavender industry is the distillery building, which has been used for a variety of purposes.

Peppermint

CROCKENHILL and Chelsfield are among the areas in Kent where peppermint, *Mentha x piperita,* was cultivated. The plant would grow profusely on light, well drained, calcareous soil, in particular where there was a considerable depth of soil lying on the chalk. Rich loam on gravel and sandy loam on gravel were also suitable. The stems and leaves provided the pungent, volatile oil and the plants produced a higher quality and quantity of oil in open, sunny situations where there was not excessive rainfall during the growing months from April to August.

The land was prepared in the autumn and winter. It was ploughed and cross-ploughed and farmyard manure used to increase the fertility of the soil. Ploughing was done so that five to six wide beds were created with an eighteen inch furrow between each of them. It was vital to clear the land of as many weeds as possible and women walked along the furrows hand-weeding the beds which could not be hoed because of the risk of severing the shoots of the peppermint.

Once ploughed the beds lay fallow for the rest of the winter. In the spring, when a fine tilth had been achieved, the tops of the beds were levelled with hand rakes and the young lengths of creeping rootstock were dibbled in about twelve inches apart, then firmed in as the planters worked their way along the beds.

The dark green-leaved peppermint was usually ready to be harvested in mid-August when it was twenty or so inches high. The whole of the plant above ground was harvested, either by hand using small 'mint hooks' or, if the plants were tall and upright enough, a small horsedrawn mower was used to mow the peppermint.

Harvesting had to be done in dry weather. The peppermint stems were then laid out in long, even rows, known as 'windrows' on the beds to dry. They were turned periodically like hay, to allow the air to dry the plants thoroughly. After two days, if the weather had been fine, the crop was collected into small heaps and allowed to stand for another two days. It would be turned once during that time. When dry and brittle the cut peppermint stems would be ready for distilling.

They would be heaped into one hundredweight bundles and wrapped in open ended hessian bags, tied up and taken to distilleries at Mitcham. One company that used Kent grown peppermint as well as lavender was W J. Bush of Batsworth Road, Mitcham. It was still distilling peppermint oil in the 1950s, but the premises have since been demolished. Unlike lavender the time factor between harvesting and distilling was not so important as the peppermint would retain its quality almost indefinitely.

It is believed that peppermint as a ·crop was grown for the first time at Wested Farm, Crockenhill where George Miller planted it in three fields. The crop was sufficiently successful to prompt him to grow more, which he did both at Wested Farm and at Warren Road, Chelsfield.

By 1922 Miller was farming the crop so extensively that he became known as the Peppermint King. His son, Albert, took over from him and founded Albert Miller (Swanley) Ltd in 1935 with his son, Cyril. Their 420 acres of peppermint supplied the British demand and was even exported to Europe.

After the Second World War peppermint was no longer an economic crop for the farm. By 1947 the acreage had fallen to fourteen acres, and at the time this was believed to be the largest crop of peppermint in England.

Eleven years later the last crop was harvested at Wested Farm, Crockenhill. Peppermint is still grown in herb farms in Kent but by no means on such a large scale as formerly.

Peppermint.

31

Mangolds, white mustard and woad

SOME unusual but important crops have been cultivated in the past on Romney marsh, in the Sandwich area, on the Isle of Thanet, in North Kent, the Hundred of Hoo and the Isle of Sheppey.

Mangolds, radishes and turnips were grown for the seed they produced not, as now, for their edible roots. So was black mustard which contained up to twenty-two per cent oil. Rape, now grown for its oil, was then grown as a sheep forage crop, as was white mustard, which had yellow flowers. Its name comes from the seeds, which are white.

On the Isle of Thanet and on the North Downs chalkland sainfoin, lucerne, red and white clover and trefoil were also grown, possibly as far back as the late seventeenth century. The pink flowered sainfoin and blue-violet lucerne were grown as hay or forage crops. So were the other three and in the past they would have been as colourfully conspicuous from a distance as are today's yellow rape or blue linseed.

Sainfoin and lucerne are legumes which produce pods of seed. The former was cut for hay in its first year and used as aftermath grazing for lambs in its second year. White clover and trefoil seeds were mixed together and grown as plants to be used for sheep keep.

Kohl-rabi, known also as the turnip-rooted cabbage because of the shape of its fleshy, bulbous stem, was grown like swedes and turnips and used as a cattle and sheep feed. The vegetable was introduced into agriculture in 1767 by John Reynolds who lived at Dane Court, Adisham, and was a member of a famous Kent farming family. He was nationally as well as locally renowned for his successful 'innovations' concerning crops and farming methods of the day.

One of the crop 'innovations' was kohl-rabi which was grown as a field crop to use as fodder in early spring. In those days the leafy tops were eaten by cows and if the kohl-rabi which was more frost resistant than swedes, was still in the ground, , the roots were dug out by pigs.

Woad was grown on the poor or chalky soils of West Kent. The seeds were sown in April/May in rows ten inches apart, the rows having to be periodically hoed to remove weeds. This biennial herb has yellow flowers and lance-shaped leaves which contain the blue dye, indigotine. When about ten inches high the stems were cropped to a height of about three inches to increase leaf growth and make gathering easier. The leaves were taken to a crushing mill where they were crushed by a horse-drawn roller and left to ferment. After fermentation they were kneaded into balls by hand, dried, couched, casked and conveyed to the dye factories.

Another plant grown for its dye was the yellow-flowered madder. Red dye was obtained from its roots and when mixed with indigotine from woad the colour purple was obtained.

Both woad and madder, as with sainfoin and lucerne, are nowadays sometimes found growing in waste places. They are the descendants of those once grown as a crop in that area.

Woad (*Isasis tinctoria*)

A team of oxen, possibly Kentish Red cattle, at Tenterden in the early 1900s.
Photo: Richard Filmer.

Oxen hauling a waggon at Chilham in 1904.
Photo:Nicola Pomfret

6

LIVESTOCK

The Kentish Red cattle

ALTHOUGH now extinct, the Kentish Red was the cattle breed indigenous to Kent. With the Sussex Red it may have been directly descended from the polled red cattle already existing in south-east England and found here when the Romans invaded 1,950 years ago. Alternatively, the Kentish Red may have been – with the Sussex Red, Devon and Red Poll – a descendant of the heavy red cattle brought here by the Anglo-Saxons to supplement the existing red cattle stock and to improve the breed.

There is also the possibility that examples of the polled types of red cattle found in north-west Europe were brought here by the Belgae, a Gallic tribe which had settled in southern England before Julius Caesar's army set sail from Boulogne on 26 August 55BC for Deal and Dover. The Belgae used oxen for ploughing, employing teams of four or eight to haul their heavy ploughs through stiff soil.

In the seventeenth century some Dutch cattle were imported into Kent and crossed with the Kentish Red to produce a type that became known as the Kentish Home-bred, large numbers of which were fattened for the London meat markets.

Thomas Fuller, writing in the 1640s, said of the cattle and the poultry of Kent that they were 'the largest of the land'. He mentions 'a giant ox, fed in Romney Marsh,' that was 'some six years since to be seen in London, so high that one of ordinary stature could hardly reach to the top of his back'. This was, perhaps, the same animal referred to by John Evelyn in his diary on 29 April, 1649:

'I saw in London a huge ox bred in Kent, 17 feet in length and much higher than I could reach.'

35

Daniel Defoe, who visited the area in 1725 when he was preparing one of the first county by county guide books, *A Tour Through England and Wales,* noted that almost every part of country furnished something in the way of produce for the City of London.

'From the Wild (Weald) of Kent they bring the large Kentish bullocks, famed for being generally all red and with their horns crooked inward, the two points standing one directly against the other, they are counted the largest breed in England.'

When the last Kentish Red went to market or died is not known. The breed probably suffered a gradual decline as result of a reduction in the numbers of Kentish Red bulls. Of necessity the Sussex Red would be used instead, until the pure Kentish Red was no longer a separate breed.

In their *Agriculture and Soils of Kent, Surrey and Sussex* of 1911, Hall and Russell say of the Sussex:

'The fashionable colour is a deep mahogany red with a white tip to the tail and occasionally spots of white on the belly, but light red colours are equally true and admissible. . . The Sussex are essentially grazing cattle, they are rarely milked but allowed to bring up their calves in the open . . . manifold excellencies of the Sussex cattle, their rapid growth, their hardiness and thrifty character on comparatively poor land, have never been properly appreciated outside their own district. They are not in many hands and have mostly been kept in small herds, often. handed down for generations from father to son; they have never been taken up and made conspicuous by any breeder of more than local fame with the result they have not shared in the cosmopolitan reputation and extension into new counties, that have marked the history of the Hereford, Shorthorn, etc. At the present time however, they are rising in repute and an export trade is beginning; the number of pedigree herds is also increasing, especially in Kent'.

As recently as 1967 Bryan Platt commented in his *Farming in the South-East:*

Among the beef cattle you may see most frequently will be the Sussex. This breed is native to the Weald and the marshlands of Kent, Surrey and Sussex. They are always red, with medium sized horns . . . and the supply of these animals for draft purposes from the Weald to other parts of the country continued long after the horse became popular as a working farm animal.'

Today the Sussex, with its long history in the two adjoining counties, continues to be considered one of the foremost of the beef breeds.

A Kent Black boar, *c* 1911

7

LIVESTOCK

The Kentish pigs

IN the past a number of English counties and towns had their own breed of pig, examples being the Gloucester Old Spot,the Tamworth Red, the Berkshire and the Essex Saddleback. Kent had its own pig breeds, too – the Kent Black and the Kent White.

Their origin is uncertain but probably their ancestors were the wild pigs that roamed the native woodland of the Weald. The Neolithic occupants of that area kept the better quality pigs and other livestock in enclosed areas so they would not have to organise a hunting party every time they required fresh meat. They also introduced pigs from other areas to improve their own stock.

The Saxons used the woodland of the Weald partly to maintain herds of hogs which thrived on the beechmast, acorns, and other pannage from the woodland floor. Separate enclosures, known as 'dens' or 'denns' were made in the woods so it was possible to segregate the different herds which were in the care of swineherds, or hogsherdsmen, who would drive them to new pannage when the old had been cleared. The herds were periodically culled to provide fresh meat and some of the carcases would be salted and stored for winter sustenance.

After the Conquest the Normans continued the Weald pannage practice. There are numerous references to pigs in the *Domesday Book* .Often it gives the value and size of woodland as the number of pigs it did or could support. For example the woodland at Pluckley supported 140 pigs; that at Benenden a mere five pigs.

The creation of 'dens', which had begun about 900 AD, formed the basis for settlements which eventually became villages or hamlets. Although much of the Weald terrain was difficult to cultivate by the early fourteenth century the more fertile and hospitable regions were rapidly being cleared for animal and crop husbandry.

Laws were introduced in Kent in the Middle Ages to govern rearing of swine. They had to be nose ringed so they would not uproot the earth when released on to the autumn pannage, or cause damage to a neighbour's land should they stray on to it. Anyone owning unringed swine was punished. If, for instance, an unringed pig damaged a neighbour's crops its owner would be heavily fined.

Herds of pigs were periodically moved on to common land to feed and their owners contributed to the wages of the swineherd employed to look after them – the amount of contribution depending on how many pigs an owner had in his herd. It was the swineherd's job to ensure the different herds stayed together and kept off private property or other crops and grazing land. At the end of their days on the commons the pigs had to be separated into herds and returned to their respective owners.

The pig as a meat animal remained basically the same until towards the end of the eighteenth century when there were attempts to improve their quality. Certain local breeds of pigs were developed, partly through crossing with the Chinese pigs which arrived here in large numbers from 1770 until 1780 imported direct from China. They had short legs and round bodies and helped greatly to improve some of the native breeds.

In Kent the rearing of large numbers of pigs, which had been an important part of the rural economy, declined as other livestock husbandry and mixed farming expanded. The rearing of small herds, however, continued on Kent farms into the early twentieth century, even smallholders keeping some pigs as part of their income raising stock.

The rural cottager would, if he could, keep pigs in a backyard sty not only to obtain meat for his family from his own efforts but also to earn money when one was sent to the butcher. Often these 'cottage pigs' were nondescript animals of not very high quality for they were all the cottager could afford to buy as piglets.

At seasonal country fairs and town and village markets attended by farmers and butchers pigs were among the livestock bought and sold. Unfortunately, unlike some of the pig rearing counties, detailed records of the early Kent pigs were not kept, nor is much known about what steps, if any, were taken to improve the Kent Black pig breed.

A number of counties had their own local breed, with characteristics and qualities that were favoured by farmers and consumers in that area. Some examples of the local breeds were of high enough quality to be used as breeding stock with the result that the breed stayed pure and became 'set.' There is no reason to suppose this was not the case in Kent, the Kent Black and Kent White having qualities favoured by consumers in the county.

The Kent Black pig, sometimes also called the Black Kent, resembled what was known as the Old English Long Black, which had drooping ears. About seventy-five years ago, in answer to an inquiry from a student, (whose son told me the details) a Wye College lecturer claimed to the class of farming students there was no such breed as the Kent Black. It was, according to him, nothing more than a local name for the more familiar and common Large Black, whose history had been traced back to the Old English hog of the sixteenth century.

Farming history correspondent, Mr C F Hickman of Stelling Minnis, whose father and grandfather farmed for some sixty years, from about 1870, at Moat Farm, Ivychurch, Romney Marsh, and kept Kent Black pigs, told me that apart from colour there was little resemblance between the

Kent Black and Large Black. The Kent Black had smaller ears, far less hair which was of a much finer texture, and stood higher off the ground.

In the opinion of the late Ralph Whitlock, a farming and rural history expert, the Kent Black was possibly a similar breed to the Dorset Black, one of a number of several black breeds confined to southern and eastern counties – another being the Small Black formerly known as the Black Suffolk.

There was also a Kent White pig. It was rather long-legged, narrow-backed and similar to the early Suffolk White type. It had medium length ears, was very hairy and said to have a thick rind or skin.

By 1911, according to a Board of Agriculture Report, pig breeding did not form a very important feature of the agriculture of the area . There was little or no bacon curing and what pigs were raised were sold in the main for local consumption

'In East Kent the Old English Long Black pig is still common.', said the report. 'Several herds exist where the strain has long been kept pure and the animals true to type and, as the good qualities of this excellent bacon pig have been recognised, it is to be hoped that it will become more general. None of the old unmixed Kent herds have been registered, however, so it is probable they will die out as a separate breed and become merged in the general Large Black breed.' It seems likely that this is what did happen.

In 1884 the National Pig Breeders Association was formed and began to establish herd books for the pedigree breeds. Some of the breeds also had their own independent county or national society. The Kent Black was not among them, although the Large Black Pig Society had been formed in 1899. Prior to this, without registers of pedigrees, the breeding of pig types was haphazard with variable characteristics being obtained from local pig-breeds.

When and where the last Kent Black pig existed I have been unable to find out. Mr Hickman thought it was about 1918 when his father wanted a Kent Black boar for his Kent Black herd, but was unable to obtain one and was very annoyed at having to make do with a Large Black boar instead.

A Buff Orpington cock and hen, *c* 1919.

8

LIVESTOCK

The Orpington poultry

THE Buff Orpington is a world famous breed. It is not bred commercially in Britain today, but among poultry fanciers it is considered a regal bird, majestic in appearance, the Rolls-Royce of the Fancy Breeds. The plumage is orange-buff; the comb, wattles and eye patch bright scarlet; the beak and legs pinkish-white. As a general purpose breed for poultry farming the Buff Orpington was supreme – ideal for the table, of heavy bone that grew slowly but had a good quality flesh particularly white and juicy with plenty of breast meat. It was a reliable winter layer of brown eggs. As a sitting parent the hen was an excellent, attentive mother to her chicks.

The Buff Orpington has a docile character. They tend to be gross feeders and put on too much flesh if kept intensively and in the past did better when allowed to range freely. The other Orpingtons had similarly distinguishing characteristics, both as poultry birds and in exhibitions.

The first, introduced in 1886 by William Cook, was the Black Orpington. Cook was born at St Neots, Huntingdonshire in 1849 but little is known of his early life there. His first job was at Chislehurst, probably as a coachman, and in the late 1860s he began poultry farming.He soon developed an expert knowledge of poultry breeding and by 1869 he had written *W Cook's Poultry Breeder and Feeder*, although it was not published for general sale until 1882.

In 1886 he was living at Tower House, Orpington, and it was there, and in that year, he bred, introduced and first exhibited his Black Orpington. It was developed from the Croad Langshan, Indian Game, Black Minorca and Black Rock breeds and he named it after the place where it emerged from the egg.

The Black Orpington proved popular with poultry farmers and this encouraged Cook to introduce his equally successful White Orpington in 1888. It was a strikingly attractive breed with snow-white plumage, white legs, and a crimson comb and wattle. These Orpingtons had advantages over other breeds then being produced, but their success was also due to Cook's aptitude for business when poultry farming was becoming a commercial venture on its own account in various parts of the country rather than as a sideshoot from other forms of farming. Sometimes unscrupulous poultrymen fraudulently sent unreliable birds and sittings of eggs to customers. Cook, however, sent his birds on approval and he soon gained a reputation for fair dealing. In consequence his business thrived and grew too large for Tower House. In 1890 he moved to Walden Manor, which he re-named Orpington House, at St Mary Cray. It had accommodation for several thousand birds and a fowl hospital with an 'operating house'.

In 1886 he had started his own magazine, the *Poultry Journal,* and he also wrote for other specialist magazines and lectured on poultry breeding. With so many demands on his time he decided to hand over the poultry farm business to his daughter Elizabeth, the eldest of his five children. She, assisted by her brothers and sister, soon became a skilful breeder and in 1907 introduced the Cuckoo Orpington and the Blue Orpington.

THE
POULTRY JOURNAL

HOW TO MAKE) (POULTRY PAY.

DEVOTED ENTIRELY TO THE INTERESTS OF POULTRY KEEPERS

Vol. 35.—No. 403   FEBRUARY, 1924.   6d. Monthly (5/- per annum by post)

The Original Poultry Journal—Published Monthly Since 1886 by WILLIAM COOK & SONS, Poultry Breeders, ST. MARY CRAY The Originators of the ORPINGTON FOWLS and DUCKS

THE HOME OF ALL THE ORPINGTONS

Special Notice is drawn to the fact that all letters intended for **WILLIAM COOK & SONS**—*the publishers of this paper for the past 38 years*—should be clearly addressed to **ST. MARY CRAY** and no mention whatever be made of Orpington on the Envelope.

Photo: A G Turner

43

The even more successful Buff Orpington was developed at Orpington House and exhibited at the National Dairy Show in 1894. To achieve it Cook first mated Golden Spangled Hamburgh cocks with Coloured Dorking hens. They produced pullets of a reddish-brown colour which were mated with a Buff Cochin cock.

In 1897 Cook introduced another breed – the Diamond Jubilee Orpington – and Queen Victoria was 'graciously pleased' to accept a pen of them from him.

When Cook's eldest son, William Henry Cook, left the family firm at Orpington House and, with a loan from his father, bought Elm Cottage (now Elmdene, 51 Derry Downs), St Mary Cray, he also set up as a poultry farmer. Cook Senior, aided by his other daughter, Catherine, continued breeding experiments with chickens and now with ducks. They introduced the Blue Orpington and Buff Orpington ducks, and the Speckled Orpington chicken. In 1902 Cook was awarded the Poultry Club Medal for his services to poultry farming.

By now Cook was travelling to other countries on business and had established poultry farms in South Africa and North America. Tragically, on 25 June, 1903, his wife, Jane, was killed in a gas explosion at Elm Cottage and a year to the day later Cook collapsed and died at Skegness where he had gone for a short holiday on his return from the States.

Elizabeth continued to run William Cook and Sons at Orpington House and carried on the experiments which resulted in the Cuckoo Orpington and Blue Orpington. She also lectured and continued publishing and editing the *Poultry Journal*. Eventually she bought out her brothers and sister and took sole charge of the business – even making use of the then-new airlines to export her poultry around the world.

Tragedy struck the family for a third time in 1933. Elizabeth was knocked down and killed in an accident involving a car in Bromley High Street and the firm ceased trading.

Today there are enthusiastic fancy poultry breeders dedicated to continuing the breeds developed by the Cooks. One is the Orpington Club, the other, the Buff Orpington Club. In December, 1986, they jointly held a special centenary year show of the breeds at Stafford to commemorate William Cook and his achievements.

The Kent sheep ewe is a good mother. *Photo: Richard Filmer.*

9
LIVESTOCK
The Kent sheep

THE Kent sheep, usually called the Romney Marsh sheep from the area where it was and is predominant, is probably the most widely known of all the different types of livestock associated with the county. The origin of the breed is uncertain. It is almost certainly Flemish – for it resembles the Flanders sheep of the past and is quite unlike the Down and Heath sheep breeds of southern England and elsewhere – plus it was possibly introduced into Kent through trade contacts with Flanders.

However, it is likely the suitable areas of Kent, including those reclaimed to become Romney Marsh, sustained a sheep population during the Roman occupation, supplying the wool known to have been exported to Rome.

Remains of a type of sheep that lived in the Saxon period have been discovered at West Hythe but these animals had only a superficial resemblance to the Romney sheep of the later period. The earliest known records of sheep in the area are an Anglo-Saxon Charter of 706 AD when sheep were not only kept for their wool but also their milk from which cheese was made.

By the end of the sixteenth century more land had been reclaimed from the sea and its rich silt produced bountiful grazing pasture with a resultant increase in the Kent sheep flocks. Inventories of the time show Romney Marsh sheep flocks were three times greater than flocks in other parts of Kent, with the possible exception of the Isle of Sheppey.

It was originally the practice to allow the pasture grass to grow long and and then in the late eighteenth century it was realised that the Kent sheep do not want a long bite and so greater numbers of sheep were introduced to keep the grass low cropped. In winter the pasture 'carried' two to three sheep per acre; in summer six to eight sheep and lambs.

A characteristic of the breed is that they do not congregate together when feeding but disperse so the grass is evenly grazed and it appears as if mown by a mower. Another important trait is the ewes are good foragers and if necessary will scrape away snow to obtain food.

They spend the winter in Romney Marsh and the other marsh pastures in Kent, lambing about second week in April, so there was a lush grass growth for the lambs when weaned. The lambs were usually shorn at same time as the ewes, providing from six to eight pounds of quality wool – the belief being they will then fatten more quickly. If the lambs were to be sold in August they would be shorn before the ewes so the extra growth of wool would, hopefully, improve their appearance and sale price.

At about the end of July or early August, at the turn of this century, lambs unlikely to survive the winter were moved from the Marsh to farms on the Downs and uplands of Kent, Sussex and Surrey, their owners paying a sum per score to the upland farmer hiring out his pasture for this purpose. If the hired pasture was not too far away the lambs were moved by road but from greater distances they would sent by special trains hired from the nearest railway station. On the uplands the lambs were wintered on grass-land cut for hay and on which no sheep had previously grazed. Some farmers put them on grass with hay or on turnips with some oil cake and corn.

William Marshall, in *The Rural Economy of the Southern Counties* of 1798, said the practice of feeding 'cake' to sheep and lambs being fattened on turnips, began in Kent.

Of farming around Maidstone he wrote:

'In the fatting of sheep the only peculiarity of practice which struck me in the dis-tinct wider view was that of employing oil cake as an ordinary material or food of fatting sheep,a practice which I understand, has been followed for half a century. It is given to them in covered troughs, some of them ingeniously constructed, in the field, either with a full bite of grass or with hay, also with turnips and perhaps an addition of hay. In either case it is a practice well calculated to forward the condition of the sheep and to improve the land on which it is used.'

In his *An Old Gate of England,* published in 1917, A G Bradley describes Romney Marsh as the finest sheep land in Britain.

'An even distribution of some 150,000 sheep in so small an area is to be seen nowhere else. It may be noted that all the lambs are removed from the Marsh in autumn to upland farms and brought back in April as tegs (sheep in their second year). This relieves the pressure when the grass is not growing and gives the young sheep a better chance to mature. May is an anxious month on the Marsh with sheep farmers who have to stock their pastures on the estimate of a normal season. If the rains hold off for the very weeks when most wanted the feebly growing young grasses get bitten down so close they cannot respond to the show-ers when these eventually fall. The Romney Marsh sheep are sometimes crossed with the Southdown. The origin of the breed is lost in the mists of time, though a theory exists upon the Marsh that, owing to their amphibious qualities, Noah shipped a pair upon the Ark as more likely to survive the voyage than any other sort. But in early days cattle and pigs (the latter only as summer grazers before the mast in the upland woods) shared the Marsh with the sheep in larger numbers than they do now.

'The polite palate professes a distaste for Romney Marsh mutton as too coarse. With the craze for small mutton which became universal in the eighties large mutton fell out of demand. The local gourmet, however, will tell you that Marsh mutton in summer and autumn is the primest of meats.'

Early June could also be a worrying time for sheep farmers. June 10 was a traditional date to start shearing Kent sheep, unless the weather was wet

Hand-shearing a Kent sheep on Romney Marsh in 1975.
Photo: Richard Filmer.

which delayed shearing as it was vital the fleece was dry when the sheep were sheared. In the past it was also customary to wash the sheep in late May or early June to clean the fleece just before shearing as this would command a higher sale price, but which also meant several days had to be allowed for the sheep to 'dry out'. So it was hoped June would be warm and sunny.

In the later eighteenth century the Kent or 'Romney' was 'a coarse, hardy, long-woolled sheep well esteemed by the butchers despite the inferior quality of the mutton.' Even so, William Cobbett in his *Rural Rides in Kent* was moved to state:

'The wool is not greasy like that of other sheep. Indeed, the fleece is as white as a piece of writing paper.'

Efforts were made to improve the breed between 1810 and 1820 by introducing Leicester rams from Bakewell and, although local graziers opposed the plan, for a period the cross with the Leicester did produce a finer quality sheep. Later on other crosses were tried with Lincoln and Cotswold rams, but their progeny were unable to cope with the hard winters and early spring conditions on the Marsh and eventually all traces of the cross were eliminated.

One sheep farmer who attempted to improve the breed by crossing was a Mr Wall of Ashford; another was Mr Gould of Sittingbourne. They were followed at the turn of the century by Henry Rigden of Lyminge and Mr T. Powell of Lenham, their rams being the foundation of some of the best Kent Sheep flocks in the 1900s.

The Kent Sheep has a broad head between the ears, with a forelock on its hornless forehead. The neck is thick, face white with a black nose and large, white, prominent eyes. It is a long, heavy sheep, with strong bones, on short legs with black hooves. In the past inferior examples had long necks, light forequarters with flat sides high on the leg. Today's Kent sheep has a long-haired, heavy fleece, weighing about 8lbs. The wool is finer and closer than the majority of other long-woolled British sheep and is valued for hand knitting yarns, carpets, blankets, hosiery, clothing, and various craft purposes.

Wool production today, however, is secondary to obtaining fat lambs for the meat market. It is this breed's strong constitution; resistance to

Kent sheep regarding the world with expressions of kindly contentment as they wait to be sheared. *Photo: Richard Filmer*

foot rot and liver fluke; its hardiness and ability to withstand the climatic conditions of Romney Marsh which other breeds could not that make it so valuable. Not surprisingly these qualities have meant it has been in demand overseas and it has been exported to New Zealand – the first recorded shipment being in 1853 – Argentina, the Falkland Islands, Australia, South Africa, the United States and Canada, as well as to Europe.

The Kentish turn-wrest plough as illustrated in John Boys *General View of the Agriculture of Kent* published in 1794. *Photo: Richard Filmer, Kennington*

10

IMPLEMENTS

Ploughs

THE Celtic plough used in pre-Roman Britain did not have a mouldboard. It created a straight furrow but did not turn over the sliced soil to bury the weeds. The Belgae, in the last century before the Romans arrived, developed and introduced into England a heavy, furrow-turning plough that did have a mouldboard, and a coulter in front of the ploughshare. It was a wheeled plough, and depending on the state of the land, required four or eight oxen to haul it. After ploughing in one direction with the Celtic plough it was necessary to plough at right angles to break up the soil, but with the Belgae's plough, which turned the soil, cross ploughing was not necessary.

The Romans used a light plough, the *aratrun,* with two oxen on soft soil but on stiffer land they used a heavy *caruca.* The later Saxon settlers had heavy ploughs requiring teams of four or eight oxen depending on the soil. These ploughs were cumbersome to turn so the Saxons made their fields as long as possible rather than square or rectangular.

The Kent plough or Turn-wrest plough

THE wood and iron-shod ploughs of those days could not cope with the flinty, chalk soil in some areas of Kent so the Turn-Wrest (pronounced turn-rees) plough was developed for use in the county. It needed four strong horses or eight oxen to pull it and on stiff, heavy land sometimes as many as sixteen oxen were required.

General purpose single-furrow horse-drawn ploughs consisted of a beam, which was the main structure of the plough, with other parts attached to it. At the forward end of the beam was the metal hake and the draught-chain by which the plough was hauled. Behind the hake was a cross-bar on which were mounted two wheels of different sizes, the larger one moving in the furrow against the soil's vertical face cut by the coulter, while the smaller wheel ran on the unploughed land side. Behind the wheels, in front of and a little above the ploughshare, was the coulter – an almost upright knife-edged length of iron long enough to part the turf or earth and make a vertical cut as it detached the furrow slice. The coulter sometimes had a hole through it into which was shackled a two foot length of chain and a drag weight. As the plough moved forward the weighted

The front view of a Kent plough

chain was dragged over the furrow slice as it was turned ensuring all sur-face material was completely buried.

At the opposite end of the beam was the two curved handles or stilts by which the ploughman controlled the plough. The metal body was bolted to the beam towards the rear end of the plough and fitted to its underside was the slade, a metal plate that slid along the bottom of the furrow. Another plate, the side-cap, was fitted on the soil face side to bear against the slice cut by the coulter. Both were detachable and could be replaced. Also bolt-ed to the body was the mouldboard, turnfurrow or breast which sustained the most friction as it turned the sliced soil over and laid the furrow. The footing or rest was bolted to the bottom edge of the mouldboard. At the front end or neck of the body was the ploughshare or sock which made the horizontal cut that separated the furrow slice from below and lifted the earth to the mouldboard.

The Kent plough or turn-wrest plough differed from this general use plough in a number of ways. The beam was some ten feet long and fitted to it by an angled oak length, sometimes known as the sheath, was a move-able mouldboard that could be changed from side to side to make it a one way plough. It could be taken off and put on the other side on hooks, the pressure of the soil against it holding it in place. The ploughshare was hor-izontal, fitted on the front end of a length of oak that was attached to the beam by another oak length called the stump at the junction with the han-dles or stilts. This ploughshare, with mouldboard removed, could also be used as a shim to clean weedy land. In front of the mouldboard, fitted to the beam, was the long, pointed, knife-edged, vertical coulter. The Kent plough also had two enormous wheels, both the same size, on a moveable axle so the wheels went up and down with the changing level of the soil being ploughed.

The turn-wrest was classed as a one way plough, although this term is misleading. Where the furrow is turned over one way, normally to the right in ordinary ploughing, a ploughing pattern has to be organised so that on reaching the end of the furrow the plough goes to another position for the return cut. This means the groups of furrows can all be turned the same way and as the plough was taken back alongside the furrow it would turn the newly made furrow on to it or away from it, depending on which side of the first furrow it was made. To allow the plough to cut the other side on its return and turn the furrow the same way as previous furrows several systems were devised. If the change of cut is made by tilting the ploughshare the other way, the plough is called a turn-wrest as the ground wrest is turned the other way with the ploughshare, or 'a one way plough' as it turns all the furrows one way – not because it only cuts one way.

Not surprisingly, as it originated in that county, Kentish names are used for some parts known by general names elsewhere. Wreest, wreist and reece (from 'wrest', to turn or twist) were other names for the mouldboard. The ploughshare was known as the iron and was fitted by an iron socket or buck to the chap – a length of oak forming part of the base of the plough.

When farmers from other counties visited Kent they were astonished at seeing the Kent plough in use. William Marshall gives this account of his reaction to it in his *Rural Economy of England,* published in 1798.

'The plow of Kent is the most extraordinary. Like that of Norfolk it is common and peculiar to the county, except that the Kentish plow is in use on the hills of Surrey and in some parts of West Sussex. To describe this extraordinary production verbally were impossible. Its component parts and the names assigned to them, are nearly equal in number to those of the ship. A North of England farmer who has never been south of the Thames, would little suspect the purpose for which it is constructed; he would conceive it to be a carriage (a farm-cart) rather than a plow. It has a pair of wheels fully as large as the fore wheels of a moorland waggon and behind them is dragged a long, thick log of wood, which slides upon the ground as the hob or shoe of a sledge, with a beam rising high above it which a small farmer of the North would be glad of as a gate post, comprising in its various parts as much timber and other materials as would build a highland cart. This magnificent implement is called the Kentish Turn Wrest Plow.'

The Kent plough was considered to be the farming dinosaur of its day. It was heavily labour intensive in operation, according to Hall and Russell, writing in 1911:

'Every agricultural writer has inveighed against the Kent plough with its three and four horses, a boy to lead and a man to hold and every newcomerinto the county has begun his farming by replacing it by a modern iron plough. Yet he often recalls it and since the implement survives it must possess some good qualities to compensate for its acknowledged wastefulness of labour. In the first place it is very adaptable; it can be mended at home by the ordinary labourer with the tools and material that are always available; without a mouldboard and armed with a broad flat point it forms a broadsharing plough, one of the best of tools on

54

the chalk soils to get rid of surface weeds and to form a good seed bed, firm below and crumbly above. It is the extreme dryness of the East Kent country which probably accounts for the value attached to this plough; there it is of fundamental importance to maintain the subsoil in a tight, well-packed condition and the heavy sole of the plough and the trampling of the team of four horses, wasteful as they look on the light soils, are all of service in consolidating the land. Deep working also is essential in such a climate and with the Kent plough, a steady, even furrow , seven to eight, or even nine inches deep can be turned, despite the flint stones which are abundant and add greatly to the difficulty of working with a light iron plough . . . At the present day (1911) the Kent Plough still maintains its position throughout East Kent. . . On the lighter loams and sands of north and mid-Kent and in the Isle of Thanet it has been somewhat replaced by balance or double-furrow ploughs.'

These early ploughs were made by blacksmiths to suit the soil conditions of the locality and meet the demands of the ploughmen who would use them. If they could not do that they were of no use to anyone.

Handmade tools in a Kent blacksmith's shop include a half-mattock, a double sider hoe, tommy hoe, Canterbury hoe and a clump hoe. *Photo: Richard Kilmer*

Working the land

THE origin and development of the smaller implements used in various farming and horticultural tasks is obscure. At the time of the Roman occupation many familiar tools were being used. The mattock, a form of hoe, was used to break down the soil and wooden frames fitted with spikes served as a harrow to pulverise and work the soil's surface.

Hoes, reaping hooks, scythes, prongs, spades and picks, some very similar to their modern counterparts, were in general use. They, like the early ploughs, were made by the village blacksmith and he could be relied upon to adapt the design of a particular tool to perform a special task.

Numerous hoes of a general pattern were used in Kent – among them the double-sider hoe, the corn hoe, plate hoe and the half-mattock. However, there were several that were developed particularly for use in the county such as:

Canterbury or speen hoe

This was a long handled hoe with a heavy iron head that had three flat tines or speens, each tine being half an inch or so wide, with a three inch gap between their inner edges. It was an implement used in dressing each 'hill' of hop rootstock in the hop gardens. The earth was drawn away from the hop plant's crown and then a sharp bladed dressing knife, was used to cut around the 'hill'. A short handled tommy hoe with one or two curved tines was then drawn round the rootstock to hook up unwanted runners. Those still in place were cut off with the dressing knife and the Canterbury hoe was used again to draw up the earth around the hop 'hill' and cover the roots. It also came in handy for 'earthing up' potatoes.

Clod hoe or clump hoe

Similar to a Kent hoe – a heavy, two-tined or pronged hoe used for loosening weeds; making furrows; and heaping earth over rows of potatoes. Its other name is clump hoe because when it is reversed – with the tines pointing upwards – it can be used to 'clump' or strike clods of earth heavily and so reduce them to a tilth.

Kent hoe
A two-pronged hoe sometimes used instead of the Canterbury Hoe for dressing hop bines.

Peck
Similar to a Weald hoe but longer in the plate and heavier than a Plate Hoe. It is sometimes called a Half-mattock. Pecks were used in hop gardens in place of the lighter Plate hoe to hack out tough weeds growing around the hop 'hills'.

Plate hoe.
Similar to a Weald Hoe, but narrow at the 'eye' broadening in a curve to the tilling or cutting edge and a much lighter tool for general hoeing. It was also used in other counties and there are modern variations.

Tommy hoe or hop hoe.
A short handled hoe with one or two curved tines, speens or prongs that were drawn through the soil in a circle close to the hop bine's rootstock to find unwanted runners

Weald hoe
A medium shafted hoe for general use. It had an iron head from which a single flat plate, about one and half inches wide broadened to about four inches at the cutting edge. Presumably its name indicates that it was developed and used originally in the Weald of Kent and Sussex.

Hop garden implements

Hop dog
A V-shaped piece of iron, with a series of teeth cut in it, attached about eighteen inches from one end of a five to seven feet long pole. When inserted into the hop 'hill' the teeth would grip the bottom of a hop pole so it could be levered out of the earth. It was used mainly in the days when hops were grown up single chestnut poles. The hop bearing pole would be taken to the pickers who then picked the hops directly from the bine into the bin.

A three wheeled version of the hop dolly or alley bodge. *Photo: Richard Filmer*

Hop dolly or alley bodge

A narrow, low, small three or more usually four wheeled wagon for carting manure along each alley between two rows of hop bines. It was drawn by a horse and the four-wheeled version was double-ended so it could be used from either direction, Sometimes a smaller version with a handcart type handle was used by pickers for haulage up and down 'their' alley.

Hop dressing knife

A sharp knife with a curved blade, which was sometimes home-made by the user from an old sickle or scythe blade.

Hop peeler

A heavy, pointed iron, round-shafted dibber-type tool used to make holes in the earth so hop poles could be set into them. A similar but shorter peeler was used for making holes for fence posts.

Hop hook or hop goad

A form of bill hook with a twelve foot long handle and the characteristic curved cutting blade having a spike on its back edge.

After a hop bine had been pulled down often the 'head', which was made up of the entangled top branches, remained on the wire or pole up which the plant had grown. The hop hook was used to cut the 'head' from the wire or pole and the spike used to push it off or lift it and lower it to the ground. Hop growing districts had their own variety of hop hooks.

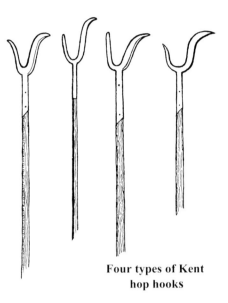

Four types of Kent hop hooks

Hop pitcher

A heavy, round shafted iron tool several feet long with a drawn out bulbous point and wooden T-handle. Like the hop peeler it was used for making holes for the hop poles. It was thrust into the earth and worked around to reach the required depth. Some had an adjustable iron 'foot' which made it easier to penetrate the earth and judge the depth of the hole. A pitcher, also known as a Dog, Hop Dog and Fold Pitcher was, like the peeler, also used for making holes for stakes and fence posts. The examples used for these purposes would sometimes be shorter than those used for making holes for hop poles.

Hop shim

The horse-drawn hop shim was a single iron 'beam' frame with five tines and straight front edged shares used for ploughing lengthways in the hop garden 'alleys'. At the forward end it had a wheel and a draught hook to which the horse or horses were harnessed. At the rear were two curved handles for the operator to guide the implement. When used as a horse-hoe for lightly tilling the earth between rows of beans, peas and other vegetables,

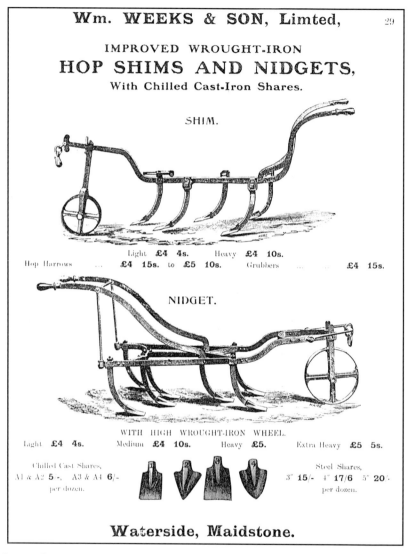

Wm. WEEKS & SON, Limted, 29

IMPROVED WROUGHT-IRON
HOP SHIMS AND NIDGETS,
With Chilled Cast-Iron Shares.

SHIM.

	Light **£4 4s.**	Heavy **£4 10s.**
Hop Harrows	**£4 15s.** to **£5 10s.**	Grubbers ... ... **£4 15s.**

NIDGET.

WITH HIGH WROUGHT-IRON WHEEL.
Light **£4 4s.** Medium **£4 10s.** Heavy **£5.** Extra Heavy **£5 5s.**

Chilled Cast Shares,
A1 & A2 **5/-**, A3 & A4 **6/-**
per dozen.

Steel Shares,
3″ **15/-** 4″ **17/6** 5″ **20/-**
per dozen.

Waterside, Maidstone.

A page from the catalogue of Weeks and Son, Maidstone, showing the price of shims and nidgets and the shapes of the shares that could be fitted to them for various purposes. *Photo: Richard Filmer.*

the tines could be adjusted to the width of the alleys or rows. A variant was the nidget (see below). It was also known as a Shove-shim.

Nidget, niggett, nidyatt, igget.

A small, triangular, heavy wooden or iron framed implement with seven to nine iron shares, used as a hoe in hop gardens. It was drawn by one or two horses along the 'alleys' of newly planted hop plants or used to winter clean established plants. As the nidget was unable to get close enough to hop 'hills' they had to be hand hoed. It was also used for cleaning between rows of beans.

In the oast house

Hop fork

A blunt-tined, wooden fork used in oasthouses to ensure hops were evenly laid for drying.

Hop sampling knife

A double-bladed knife used to cut a square out of a hop pocket to obtain a sample of the pressed hops within it.

Dried hops on the floor of the oast house. On the left is the hop press and the man second from the left is holding a scuppet.

Hop sampling pincers

Pincers with up to eight tines, used to withdraw a sample of pressed hops from a pocket.

Scubbit, scuppet, scuppit

A wood shovel with which the heaps of hops were moved around on the upper floor of the oasthouse during the drying process. The scubbit used by hop driers had a short handle and a canvas or hessian backing, but the scubbits used for moving corn on a barn floor had a longer handle and were also known as scoppels. Moving hops across the floor to where they could cool was called 'scuppeting' and shovelling the dried hops into the press and the pocket suspended below it, was known as 'scuppeting in.'

Cutting tools

Bill hook, hand bill, bill, bille.

A short-handled axe with a long, sharp cutting edge curved at one end of the blade. It was used to sever woody growth when clearing shrubby areas; to lay hedges; for pointing chestnut fencing stakes; and to split poles in hurdle making if an adze is not available. There are many local and regional variations in blade and handle length, size and shape. Some are tapered, some flat, some turned and some handles are calked to provide a better grip.

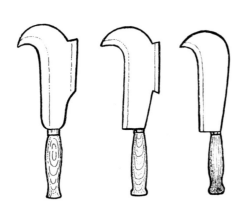

There are two types of bill hook in Kent – one has a straight cutting edge on the back of the blade and a turned handle and the second does not have the back cutting edge but does have a turned handle and is similar in pattern to the Dorset Bill.

Another form of bill hook is a slasher. This has a three foot long handle, and is longer bladed and less curved. It was used in hedge maintenance and cutting ditch foliage in the days when these jobs were done manually.

Kent axe

In the past there were numerous variations of axe shapes named after the counties in which they originated . Most survived until the end of the nineteenth century, but since then only the Kent Axe is still produced. It is a general purpose axe and there are several variations of it but basically it has a symmetrical round-shouldered blade with a curved cutting edge, pointed lugs above and below the 'eye' and a flat poll. The side of the blade is known as the 'bit' and the side of the blade between the lugs is the 'cheek'. Its weight varies from 1fibs to 8lbs.

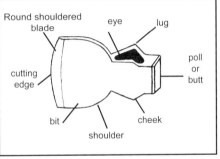

Kent felling axe

A felling axe of the Kent axe head type.

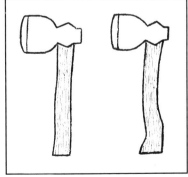

A Kent axe head and, below, axes complete with handles

Kent hatchet

This had the same head shape as the Kent Axe, but was thinner and not so heavy.

Kent side axe

The Kent Axe blade ground with a single bevel, normally on the right-hand side away from the work, so it can be used as a side axe.

BIBLIOGRAPHY

A General Survey of the Rural Economy of England – Southern Counties by William Marshall 1798.
A General View of the Agriculture of Kent by John Boys 1794.
Agriculture and Soils of Kent, Surrey and Sussex by A D Hall and E J Russell. Board of Agriculture and Fisheries 1911.
A Handbook of Hardy Fruits – Stone and Bush Fruits by Edward Bunyard. John Murray 1925.
A Short History of Farming in Britain by Ralph Whitlock. John Baker 1965.
Cultivated Fruits of Britain by F A Roach. Basil Blackwell, 1985.
Elements of Agriculture by W Fream. Twelfth edition edited by R H Biffen. John Murray 1932.
English Hops by George Clinch. McCorquodale and Company 1919.
Farming in the South-East by Bryan Platt. David Rendel 1967.
History of the Worthies of England by Thomas Fuller *c*1662.
Hops and Hop Picking by Richard Filmer. Shire Publications 1982.
The Book of Apples by Joan Morgan and Alison Richards.Ebury Press/Brogdale Horticultural Trust 1993.
The Plums of England by H V Taylor. Crosby Lockwood 1949.

Magazine article.
Fruit Growing in Kent by Henry Tydeman. *Kent County Journal* autumn 1934.